Around the World with Cricket™

Written by

Robin Frederick and Jay Tverdak

Illustration by

Kathleen McCarthy

Cricket's World

Cricket's world is full of fun and activity for Cricket and <u>you</u>. There are five other Activity Book and Tape sets like this one. And Cricket also has her own great Outfits—each one comes with a special cassette tape, too.

Cricket Activity Books and Tapes

1. Cricket's Clubhouse
2. Growing Up With Cricket
3. Cricket Takes a Vacation
4. Around the World with Cricket
5. Cricket Goes Camping
6. Holiday Fun with Cricket

Cricket Outfits and Tapes

1. School Time
2. Time for Outdoor Fun
3. Party Time
4. Indoor Play Time
5. Sleepy Time
6. Time for Health and Exercise

Hi, this is Cricket talking to you! There are so many things to do in this book, we better get started right away. You'll need crayons or felt pens, pencils, scissors, white glue, tape, construction paper and white paper for tracing—plus a few other things I'm sure you can find around the house.

Are you ready?

Here we go!

I want to introduce you to some friends of mine. They're going to guide us on our trip around the world. You'll be meeting them again in this book, so say "Hello."

In the pictures below, my friends are saying "Hello!" in the languages they speak at home. See if you can read what they're saying. If you do, then you'll know six more ways to say "Hello!"

4

B efore we go any further on our trip around the world, I thought we ought to know what our own country looks like. So let's make a map of the United States. You know what they say: See America first!

Here's what you need:
    a piece of paper you can trace with a pencil
    colored pencils or felt pens
    a ball point pen

And here's what you do:
1. place your paper over the map pictured on the next page, then trace its outline
2. trace the outlines of all the states
3. color in the states with different colors
4. copy the names of the states onto your own map

6

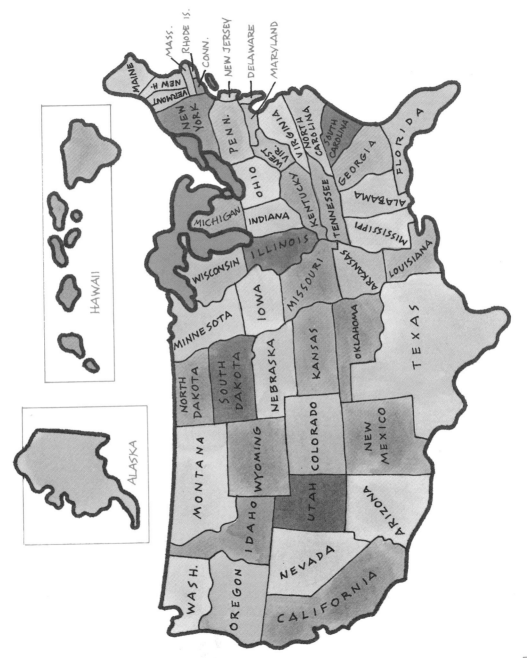

MASS.
RHODE IS.
CONN.
NEW JERSEY
DELAWARE
MARYLAND
MAINE
NEW H.
VERMONT
NEW YORK
PEN.
OHIO
WEST VIRGINIA
VIRGINIA
NORTH CAROLINA
SOUTH CAROLINA
GEORGIA
FLORIDA
ALABAMA
MISSISSIPPI
KENTUCKY
TENNESSEE
MICHIGAN
INDIANA
ILLINOIS
WISCONSIN
IOWA
MISSOURI
ARKANSAS
LOUISIANA
MINNESOTA
NEBRASKA
KANSAS
OKLAHOMA
TEXAS
NORTH DAKOTA
SOUTH DAKOTA
WYOMING
COLORADO
NEW MEXICO
MONTANA
IDAHO
UTAH
ARIZONA
WASH.
OREGON
NEVADA
CALIFORNIA
HAWAII
ALASKA

7

My friend Madeline is lost! She has to meet her classmates at the Eiffel Tower <u>a dix heures</u> — that's ten o'clock! See if you can help her get through the crowded streets of Paris. Only one street will take her straight to the Eiffel Tower. Trace it with your finger.

ENTRÉ INTERDIT!

y pen pals are back again! And this time they've asked me to help them sort out their mixed-up hats. Can you help? Just trace your finger from each of the pen pals to the right hat. Thanks a lot!

I love the different colors of the flags from all over the world. I collect flag cards and flag stickers and flag stamps. I even have flags that I made myself! I'll show you how to make them a little bit later (on page 12). But first, let's make the flag of the U.S.A.—the stars and stripes!

Here's what you need:
    3 pieces of construction paper (white, blue and red)
    a pencil
    a ruler
    scissors
    white glue
    a box of star stickers from the stationery store

And here's what you do:
1. on the blue construction paper, measure and draw a rectangle 3½ inches wide by 5 inches long
2. cut out your rectangle, then glue it in the corner of the white construction paper (see the picture on the next page)
3. on the red construction paper, measure and draw 4 strips ½ inch wide by 6 inches long
4. cut out your strips, then paste them next to the blue rectangle
5. on the red construction paper, measure and draw 3 strips ½ inch wide by 11 inches long
6. cut out your strips, then paste them underneath the blue rectangle
7. stick a total of 50 stars onto the blue rectangle, making 5 rows of 6 stars and 4 rows of 5 stars (just like in the picture on the next page)

You can tape your American flag to your bedroom wall. Or you can make a flagpole out of a yardstick or an old broom-handle.

Now that you've made your American flag, let's make a whole bunch of flags from countries around the world.

Here's what you need:
   white index cards (the kind with no lines)
   a pencil
   a ruler
   colored pencils or felt pens
   tape

And here's what you do:
1. pick a flag, then use your pencil and ruler to draw its design on both the front and back of an index card
2. color your flag just like in the picture on the next page
3. repeat steps #1 and 2 for each flag you make

You can tape your flags to straws or pencils. Or tape them all in a row to a piece of string, then hang the banner up in your room!

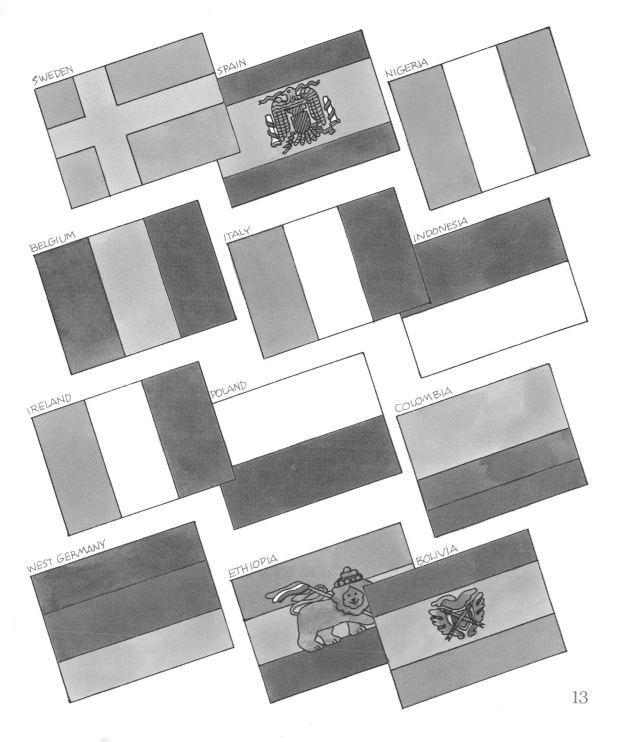

SWEDEN
SPAIN
NIGERIA
BELGIUM
ITALY
INDONESIA
IRELAND
POLAND
COLOMBIA
WEST GERMANY
ETHIOPIA
BOLIVIA

13

There are seven continents in the world. I haven't visited them all, but I <u>have</u> visited the zoo. That's where I saw each of these animals. See if you can match each animal to the continent he comes from.

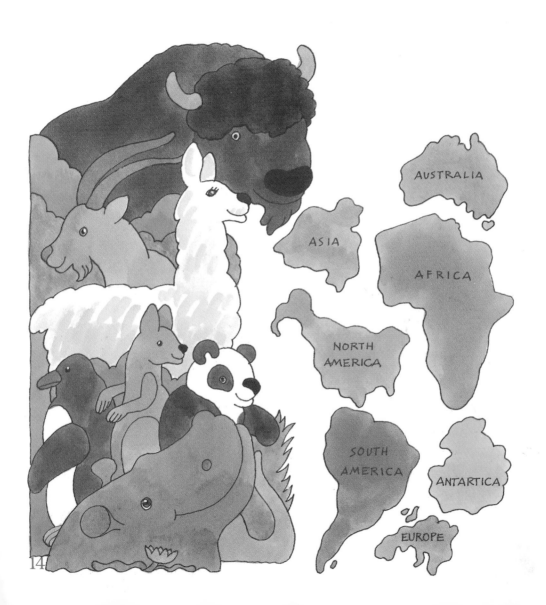

On the continent of Africa, there are many animals that are not found anywhere else. Except in zoos! Often, the animals live near each other in the same part of the jungle. But in the picture below, all the animals are hiding from the lion. See if you can find the 7 different African animals hidden in the picture.

If you need them, the answers are on page 24. But don't tell the lion!

A top is a toy that children all over the world like to play with. You can make a top of your own. It's easy! Just don't get dizzy when you spin it!

Here's what you need:
- a piece of white paper you can trace with
- a piece of light cardboard
- a pencil
- crayons or felt pens
- scissors
- a short pencil with a point that's not too sharp

And here's what you do:
1. place the white paper over the picture on the next page, then trace its outline (don't forget to trace the tiny circle in the center)
2. cut out your circle
3. place your tracing on the cardboard, then draw around its edge
4. cut out your new cardboard circle
5. draw designs on your cardboard circle, then color them any way you like
6. place the paper circle over the cardboard circle, then stick the short pencil through the tiny circle in the center
7. take off the paper circle and spin your top!

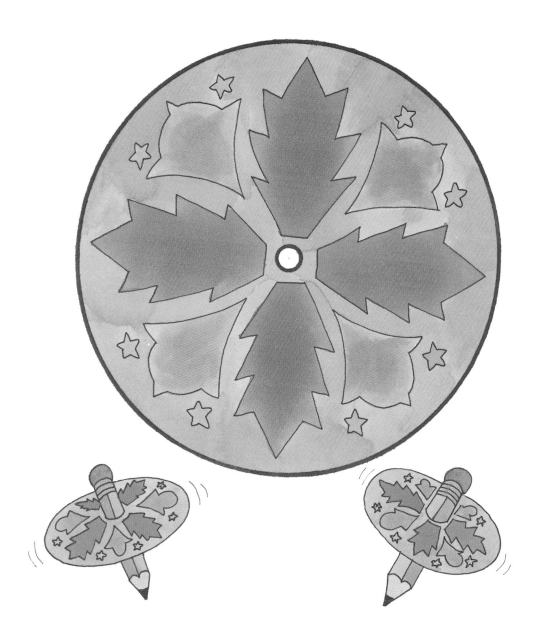

When I visited my friend Leilani in Hawaii, the first thing she did was put a beautiful string of fresh flowers around my neck. It was called a "lei". That's pronounced just like the "lay" in "Lay this book down now, and get ready to make a lei!"

Here's what you need:
   3 pieces of different-colored construction paper
   a pencil
   a ruler
   scissors
   tape

And here's what you do:
1. cut about 25 strips of construction paper, an inch wide
2. tape the first strip end-to-end
3. put the next strip through the loop of the first strip, then tape it end-to-end
4. repeat step #3 with the rest of the strips

Put the lei around your neck and try to dance the hula—just like Leilani and me. I bet you'll have fun!

19

N ow that we've been to Hawaii (where it's always nice and warm), let's go to Alaska—where it's always nice and cold! My friend Ootek lives near the North Pole. He sent me a picture of a Totem Pole his grandfather made a long time ago. Why don't you make a totem pole of your own?!

Here's what you need:
   3 empty cereal, cracker or cookie boxes (a big one, a medium-sized one, and a small one)
   poster paints
   paint brushes
   tape

And here's what you do:
1. paint the front, back and sides of each of the 3 boxes with any kind of faces you want: animal faces, bird faces or monster faces, just like in the picture on the next page
2. stack the medium-sized box on top of the large box, then tape them together
3. stack the small box on top of the medium-sized box, then tape them together.

It's almost time to say "Goodbye" to all our new friends, so let's have a farewell party. And since every party needs music, let's make a couple of musical instruments. How about an African drum, for starters?

Here's what you need:
   an empty, round oatmeal box
   tape
   poster paints
   paintbrushes

And here's what you do:
1. tape the lid onto the box
2. paint colorful designs on your drum, just like the ones in the picture

You can tape a feather to the side of your drum, or cut out pictures from old magazines and glue them on. Use a tablespoon for a drumstick.

Now let's make a pair of Mexican maracas.

Here's what you need:
   2 empty spice jars
   about a cup of uncooked rice

And here's what you do:
1. fill one jar half-full with rice
2. fill the other jar three-quarters-full with rice
3. screw the lids back on the jars
4. pick up a jar in each hand and shake, shake, shake!

22

Now that we've finished our trip around the world, let's say "Goodbye" to the friends we met at the beginning of our journey. They're all saying "Goodbye" to us in the languages they speak at home. See if you can read what they're saying. If you do, then you'll know six more ways to say "Goodbye"!

So long!

Kwa heri!

Sayonara!

Adios!

Au revoir!

Aloha!

nswers:

Page 5.
Li owns a Pekingese
Ootek owns a Malamute
Juanita owns a chihuahua
Natalia owns a Samoyed
Rory owns a terrier
Heidi owns a St. Bernard

Page 9.
Li owns the blue cap
Ootek owns the fur cap with earflaps
Juanita owns the sombrero
Natalia owns the Astrakhan cap
Rory owns the tam-o-shanter
Heidi owns the Alpine hat

Page 14.
the bison lives in North America
the Alpine goat lives in Europe
the panda lives in Asia
the llama lives in South America
the penguin lives in Antarctica
the kangaroo lives in Australia

Page 15.
a monkey
a snake
a zebra
a leopard
a giraffe
a rhinoceros